D0718475

Also available in Beaver by
Jennifer and Graeme Curry

The Beaver Book of Revolting Rhymes

And by Jennifer Curry

The Beaver Book of Skool Verse
More Skool Verse
Mary Had a Crocodile

My Name, My Poem

Compiled by
Jennifer and Graeme Curry

Illustrated by John Richardson

BEAVER BOOKS

For GLORIA, with love

A Beaver Book
Published by Arrow Books Limited

62–5 Chandos Place, London WC2N 4NW

An imprint of Century Hutchinson Ltd

London Melbourne Sydney Auckland
Johannesburg and agencies throughout the world

First published by Hutchinson Children's Books 1986
Beaver edition 1987

Text © in this collection Jennifer and Graeme Curry 1986
Illustrations © John Richardson 1986

Made and printed in Great Britain
by Anchor Brendon Ltd
Tiptree, Essex

ISBN 0 09 948030 1

Introduction

On my first day at school the teacher asked us all to stand up and tell the class our names. When we had finished she found that there were three Grahams. The other two were spelt 'Graham' and I was spelt 'Graeme' but we all sounded the same. So she asked us if we had any other Christian names. Graham Brown's middle name was 'John', but there was already a John in the class. Graham Porter's other name was 'Arnold' but there was an Arnold Baxter sitting just behind him. My middle name was 'Peter', and since there wasn't a single Peter in the class that became my *school* name for the next six years. I was still called Graeme at home. My parents called me Graeme, and so did my brother, and my Gran and Grandpa. But at school, I was Peter.

It was very confusing. I like the name Peter; some of my best friends are called Peter. But I never felt like one. I felt like a Graeme. So in class, when the teacher said, 'What is the capital of France, Peter?' I just went on gazing dreamily out of the window. And when she said 'Graham, clean the blackboard,' I was out of my seat like a rocket, only to slink back again, feeling rather stupid.

I missed my name for those six years and I'm very pleased to say that now everyone calls me Graeme again. Your name is one of the most important things about you. If you lose it, you don't feel yourself at all.

This book is full of lots and lots of different names— some very unusual, like Ulysses and Xantippe, and some very well-known ones, like Mark and Sue. We hope you can find yours. You may be one of the lucky ones with a poem all to yourself, like Justin or Sharon, or you may just have a line or two in a longer poem, like Joanna or Vince. All the names are listed in the back to help you. And when you've looked for your own, then you can start on your family's names, and those of all your friends.

Names are special things. Poems are too. My Name, My Poem is packed with both of them.

G. C.

We say thank you

Tu Tu T's

Tu T's we must thank, for the help that they
    gave
In dozens of different ways.
They read, and they listened, they helped us to
    spell,
For one hundred hard-working days.
Tu T's we must thank, for all that they did
Tu help make this book fun for u,
Their names can't be found on any other page –
So thanks tu u TESSA, and thanks tu TYM tu.

J.C. & G.C.

Come home, Alexandra

Come home, Alexandra
Come home from the moor
Your supper's long been waiting
And there's darkness at the door.

Come home, Alexandra
Don't you hear the night birds call
The wind is in the chimney
And there's shadow on the wall

Come home, Alexandra
Come home by the fire
Your little sister's sleeping
And the cows are in their byre

Come home, Alexandra
You stay out far too long
Whispering with the moon
    wind
And dancing to her song.

Tom May

Allie

Allie, call the birds in,
  The birds from the sky!
Allie calls, Allie sings,
  Down they all fly:
First there came
Two white doves,
  Then a sparrow from his nest,
Then a clucking bantam hen,
  Then a robin red-breast.

Allie, call the beasts in,
  The beasts, every one!
Allie calls, Allie sings,
  In they all run:
First there came
Two black lambs,
  Then a grunting Berkshire sow,
Then a dog without a tail,
  Then a red and white cow.

Allie, call the fish up,
  The fish from the stream!
Allie calls, Allie sings,
  Up they all swim:
First there came
Two gold fish,
  A minnow and a miller's thumb,
Then a school of little trout,
  Then the twisting eels come.

Allie, call the children,
  Call them from the green!
Allie calls, Allie sings,
  Soon they run in:
First there came
Tom and Madge,
  Kate and I who'll not forget
How we played by the water's edge
  Till the April sun set.

Robert Graves

Andrew's bedtime story

I told him a tale that I adore
Called Theseus and the Minotaur,
Of how a prince with a ball of wool
   That his girl friend Ariadne gave him,
Was forced to search for a fiery bull
   Through cave and labyrinth. Keen to save him,
She said, 'Unwind the wool as you go
Through the twisting corridors down below,
And return to me safe – I love you so.'
That was the start of the tale I told,
And Andrew listened, as good as gold.

Next day when he ran home from school,
He found a ball of his mother's wool,
Unwound it, tied it to door and chair,
Along the passage and up the stair,
   Yes, everywhere.
I opened the door of my room to find
Pitschi the cat with his legs entwined,
Jane and Helen flat on the floor,
Great-aunt almost sliced at the knees
(As wire at the grocer's slices cheese),
All of them trapped. The thread I snapped,
With scissors and knife I hacked away
And set them free. But where was A?
There, in a corner lurking, laughing.
'No more of Ariadne's thread,
My boy,' I cried, 'or we'll all be dead!'
   I stalked away.

But a murderous thread not seen before
Tripped me up, and I cracked my head.

Ian Serraillier

Little wide-awake

Angela came to us out of the flowers,
God's little blossom that changed into ours.
Cloves for her fingers, and cloves for her toes,
Eyes from the succory*, mouth from the rose.

Loveliness sprang from the sisterly stocks,
Daffodils gave her those yellowy locks.
Fairies that visit her constantly meet,
Lilies and lavender making her sweet.

Cherry-pie, pansy, forget-me-not, musk,
Wake in her dawning and sleep in her dusk.
Angela came to us out of the flowers,
God's little blossom that changed into ours.

(Victorian)

*succory is another name for chicory

The blackbird

In the far corner,
close by the swings,
every morning
a blackbird sings.

His bill's so yellow,
his coat's so black,
that he makes a fellow
whistle back.

Ann, my daughter,
thinks that he
sings for us two
especially.

Humbert Wolfe

Hie, hie.

Hie, hie, says Anthony,
Puss is in the pantry,
Gnawing, gnawing, a mutton mutton-bone;
See how she tumbles it,
See how she mumbles it,
See how she tosses the mutton mutton-bone.

Anon

Little Barbara

Little Barbara went to Scarborough,
Just to buy a candelabra.
At the harbour a bear ate Barbara.
Don't you find that most macabre?

Colin West

The tale of Custard the dragon

Belinda lived in a little white house,
With a little black kitten and a little grey mouse,
And a little yellow dog and a little red wagon,
And a realio, trulio, little pet dragon.

Now the name of the little black kitten was Ink,
And the little grey mouse, she called him Blink,
And the little yellow dog was sharp as Mustard,
But the dragon was a coward, and she called him
    Custard.

Custard the dragon had big sharp teeth,
And spikes on top of him and scales underneath,
Mouth like a fireplace, chimney for a nose,
And realio, trulio daggers on his toes.

Belinda was as brave as a barrel full of bears,
And Ink and Blink chased lions down the stairs,
Mustard was as brave as a tiger in a rage,
But Custard cried for a nice safe cage.

Belinda tickled him, she tickled him unmerciful,
Ink, Blink and Mustard, they rudely called him
 Percival,
They all sat laughing in the little red wagon
At the realio, trulio, cowardly dragon.

Belinda giggled till she shook the house,
And Blink said Weeck! which is giggling for a
 mouse,
Ink and Mustard rudely asked his age,
When Custard cried for a nice safe cage.

Suddenly, suddenly they heard a nasty sound,
And Mustard growled, and they all looked
 around.
Meowch! cried Ink, and Ooh! cried Belinda,
For there was a pirate, climbing in the winda.

Pistol in his left hand, pistol in his right,
And he held in his teeth a cutlass bright,
His beard was black, one leg was wood;
It was clear that the pirate meant no good.

Belinda paled, and she cried Help! Help!
But Mustard fled with a terrified yelp,
Ink trickled down to the bottom of the household,
And little mouse Blink strategically mouseholed.

But up jumped Custard, snorting like an engine,
Clashed his tail like irons in a dungeon,
With a clatter and a clank and a jangling squirm,
He went at the pirate like a robin at a worm.

The pirate gaped at Belinda's dragon,
And gulped some grog from his pocket flagon,
He fired two bullets, but they didn't hit,
And Custard gobbled him, every bit.

Belinda embraced him, Mustard licked him,
No one mourned for his pirate victim.
Ink and Blink in glee did gyrate
Around the dragon that ate the pirate.

But presently up spoke little dog Mustard,
I'd have been twice as brave if I hadn't been
     flustered.
And up spoke Ink and up spoke Blink,
We'd have been three times as brave, we think,
And Custard said, I quite agree
That everybody is braver than me.

Belinda still lives in her little white house,
With her little black kitten and her little grey
     mouse,
And her little yellow dog and her little red
     wagon,
And her realio, trulio little pet dragon.

Belinda is as brave as a barrel full of bears,
And Ink and Blink chase lions down the stairs,
Mustard is as brave as a tiger in a rage,
But Custard keeps crying for a nice safe cage.

Ogden Nash

Ben

Ben, in his wide red shorts
with pockets deep for stones
walks on with a stoop.
His stub antennae nose
surveys, seeks out
the green and marble chips –
the churchyard sweets.
Ben, the menace, in his
red hooped tee shirt
rattles down
the hoggin path,
head of dandelion
flying seed,
sun silvered,
weightless,
past the close cropped
banks of turf
and hazelled headstones
with his prize.

Barry Norrington

Burger bun

Benny bit a burger bun.
The burger bun bit Benny.
Benny bit it back again.
It only cost a penny.

Anon

Brian

Brian is a baddie,
As nasty as they come.
He terrifies his daddy
And mortifies his mum.

One morning in December
They took him to the zoo,
But Brian lost his temper
And kicked a kangaroo.

And then he fought a lion
Escaping from its pit.
It tried to swallow Brian
Till Brian swallowed it!

Yes, Brian is a devil,
A horrid little curse –
Unlike his brother Neville
Who's infinitely worse!

Doug Macleod

Caroline in cotton rags

Here's Catherine in crinoline,
And Celia in silk,
And Claudia in dimity
With skin as white as milk.

And yet with all this finery,
This taffeta and lace,
It's Caroline in cotton rags
Who has the fairest face.

Colin West

Charles

Charles was super
Charles was sleek
Head of school
and strong as teak
Charles was leader
Charles was best
Led the school
With style and zest.
Charles was kingly
Charles was smart
Kindly eye
and golden heart.
  He led through storms
  and placid days
  with towering strength
  and peaceful ways.
          He was . . .

   the Prince of Whales.

Peter Dixon

Kite-flying

Years ago,
  I had a proper kite,
A little piece of
  Dark blue sky
With a starry tail.
  It soared as high
As my dreams;
  Then, dipping, settled
On a steady flight.
  It wasn't any fun
If someone else took it
  And felt the strains,
I danced around
  And begged it back . . .

Except for Charlie,
  I try not to help,
But watch her joys
  Climb up along
The line I hand
  To her.

Rosemary Cowan

Choosing a name

I have got a new-born sister;
I was nigh the first that kissed her.
When the nursing woman brought her
To papa, his infant daughter,
How papa's dear eyes did glisten!
She will shortly be to christen:
And papa has made the offer,
I shall have the naming of her.

Now I wonder what would please her,
Charlotte, Julia, or Louisa.
Ann and Mary, they're too common;
Joan's too formal for a woman;
Jane's a prettier name beside;
But we had a Jane that died.
They would say, if 'twas Rebecca,
That she was a little Quaker.
Edith's pretty, but that looks
Better in old English books;
Ellen's left off long ago;
Blanche is out of fashion now.
None that I have named as yet
Are so good as Margaret.
Emily is neat and fine.
What do you think of Caroline?

Colin

When you frown at me like that, Colin,
And wave your arm in the air,
I know just what you're going to say:
'Please, Sir, it isn't fair!'

It isn't fair
On the football field
If their team scores a goal.
It isn't fair
In a cricket match
Unless you bat *and* bowl.

When you scowl at me that way, Colin,
And mutter and slam your chair,
I always know what's coming next:
'Please, Sir, it isn't fair!'

It isn't fair
When I give you a job.
It isn't fair when I don't.
If I keep you in
It isn't fair.
If you're told to go out, you won't.

When heads bow low in assembly
And the whole school's saying a prayer,
I can guess what's on your mind, Colin:
'Our Father . . . it isn't fair!'

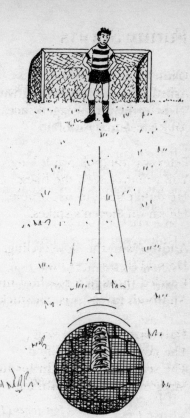

It wasn't fair
In the Infants.
It isn't fair now.
It won't be fair
At the Comprehensive
(For first years, anyhow).

When your life reaches its end, Colin,
Though I doubt if I'll be there,
I can picture the words on the gravestone now.
They'll say: IT IS NOT FAIR.

Allan Ahlberg

I say, Mummy, there's Mrs Geyser
And doesn't she look pretty sick?
I bet it's because Mona Lisa
Was hit on the hock with a brick.

———

Miss Blewitt says Monica threw it,
But Monica says it was Joan,
And Joan's very thick with Miss Blewitt,
So Monica's sulking alone.

And Margaret failed in her paces,
Her withers got tied in a noose,
So her coronets caught in the traces
And now all her fetlocks are loose.

Oh, it's me now. I'm terribly nervous.
I wonder if Smudges will shy.
She's practically certain to swerve as
Her Pelham is over one eye.

Oh wasn't it naughty of Smudges?
Oh, Mummy, I'm sick with disgust.
She threw me in front of the Judges,
And my silly old collarbone's bust.

John Betjeman

Happy birthday, Dilroy!

My name is Dilroy,
I'm a little black boy
And I'm eight today.

My birthday cards say
It's great to be eight
And they sure right
Coz I got a pair of skates
I want for a long long time.

My birthday cards say
Happy Birthday, Dilroy!
But, Mummy, tell me why
they don't put a little boy
that looks a bit like me.
Why the boy on the card so white?

John Agard

Not so gorgeous

Dorothy's drawers are creamy gauze;
   Lil's are long and slack;
Tonia's tights are crocheted whites;
   Jennifer Jane's are black.

Betty's bloomers are slaty grey,
   And she tucks her skirt inside;
Polly's are pink – since yesterday –
   I think she's had them dyed.

Sarah's silks were awf'ly dear –
   The best her mum could get;
And (may I whisper it in your ear?)
   Nancy's knickers are wet!

Sue's are blue, and Prue's are too,
   And little Pam's are sweet;
While naughty Meg has lost a leg,
   And Tilly has torn her seat.

Swanky Maisie's are trimmed with daisies
   And patched with coloured stuffs;
But those on Milly look awful silly –
   They sort of flap their cuffs!

Jill's have frills, and Pat's are plain,
  With a button in case they fall;
And (may I whisper once again?)
  I haven't a pair at all!

                              J. A. Lindon

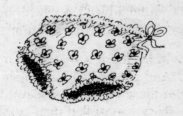

One boy . . .

Edward and Teddy, Eddie and Ned,
When the dawn broke, jumped out of bed,
Played in the sunshine, swam in the sea,
Laughed in the wind, ran home to tea.
But when the day ended, strange as it seems,
Only one boy lay down to sweet dreams.

. . . One girl

Elizabeth, Elspeth, Betsy and Bess,
They all went together to seek a bird's nest;
They found a bird's nest with five eggs in,
They all took one and left four in.

Anon

Picnic

Ella, fell a
Maple tree.
Hilda, build a
Fire for me.

Teresa, squeeze a
Lemon, so.
Amanda, hand a
Plate to Flo.

Nora, pour a
Cup of tea.
Fancy, Nancy,
What a spree!

Hugh Lofting

From The wicked children's alphabet

Emily, the Captain's daughter,
Loved to play about with water,
So she filled her bath with mice.
Swimming round they looked so nice.

Cousin Yves, across the Channel
Came to stay, and lost his flannel.
Feeling for the soap he found
Twenty mice were crawling round.

So he put the Hoover on,
And, hey presto! – they had gone!

Pauline Mitchell

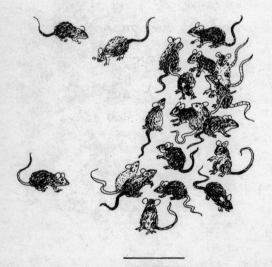

Emma

Emma's shy, she's peeping
Around the chair – keeping
Quiet as a mouse

Emma's shy, she's listening
Warm brown eyes a-glistening
It's strange at Grannie's house

Emma's shy, she's kneeling
Just gazing at the ceiling
Hoping for a sweet

Emma's shy, they're talking
Ignoring her, and walking
By on grown-up feet

Emma's shy, she's growing
And secretly she's knowing
That one day she'll
                  be
                  BIG

Mary Rudin

Fiona

Please clean your room, Fiona,
Please try to set it straight,
Please clean it now, Fiona,
It really cannot wait.

Fiona doesn't listen,
Fiona doesn't hear,
Besides, it can't need doing,
She did it just last year,

Fiona's getting bored now,
Just sitting on her own,
She goes to Mummy's bedroom,
And creeps in all alone,

Picking up a lipstick tube,
She covers lips and chin,
She smiles at her reflection,
And grins a little grin,

A dress from out the wardrobe,
And from a box a hat,
A fur coat then to finish,
Gosh, Mummy will like that,

But Mummy doesn't like it,
Her face goes all bright red,
She screams at young Fiona,
And packs her off to bed,

The moral of this poem,
For Fionas everywhere,
When wearing Mummy's clothing,
First make sure she isn't there.

Paul Sayers

Fantastic Frances

Frances was a beauty, Frances was a joy,
Frances turned the head
Of every passing boy.

Frances was a scholar, Frances did her work,
Frances learnt her lessons and
Was never known to shirk.

Frances was an athlete, Frances was a sport,
Frances was the star
Of any tennis court.

Frances was a singer, she danced and acted too . .
I wish my name was Frances,
Don't you?

Jenny Sinclair

Helicopter

Heli, Heli, Heli,
Copter,
Miss Brown was strolling when it stopped her;
Very, very nearly dropped her
Shopping-bag in sudden fright
At the monstrous clatter-flight.
All the men lean on their spades
And watch the flashing rotor-blades.
Gavin (watching television plays)
Yelled, 'Look, a coastal rescue chopper –
Most exciting thing for days –
Isn't it a yellow whopper?'
Like a maddened bumble-bee
It has him twisting round to see;
Makes all the village heads corkscrew
To wave a welcome to the crew,
Who nonchalant through open door
Wave as they squat upon the floor.

Gavin (and all the racing boys)
Rejoices in the noose of noise;
But stern Miss Brown now flushed with rage
Is scribbling a double page.
'Write to the paper, yes, I must;
I shall express my deep disgust.'
While in a near-by field the sheep,
A woolly, lumpy, startled heap,
Bolted,
Halted,
Cropped a
Little fainter,
Bewildered by the helicopter.

Gregory Harrison

My family

Mummy is nearly thirty,
Daddy's been there before,
My brother is four,
And I am more.
Baby Gemma's just arrived
through the door.

Simon Rainey (7)

George's pet

When George and his gorilla
Go bounding down the street,
They get respectful nods and smiles
From neighbours that they meet.

If George had owned a puppy dog,
Or else a kitty-cat,
His neighbours wouldn't notice him
With courtesy like that.

Margaret Mahy

Shaking

Geraldine now, stop shaking that cow
For heaven's sake, for your own sake
   and the cow's sake,
That's the dumbest way I've seen
To make a milk shake.

Shel Silverstein

The Maldon Mud Race

They have a Mud Race in our town.
Every year
On New Year's Day.

'It clears the old head,' they say
And laugh.
I don't know why.

It's great.

I go with my Dad.
'Come on, Giles,' he says,
'Let's watch the lads.'

Then all these men,
They jump in the mud
And run across the Flats.
There, and back again.

It's great.

Some of them get dressed up.
One's a clown
With a red nose.
Another's a ghost
In a white sheet.
One looks like a nurse
In a frock
But I know it's a man
'Cos he's got hairy legs . . .
And football boots.
They all get covered in mud.

It's great.

The last day of the holidays
Mum got me
Some new school trousers.
All thick and grey and scratchy.
'Don't pull that face,' she said.
'After the first wash they'll be

Just great.'

When Vince came
We went for a walk.
'Mind you keep clean,' Mum said.
'What'll we do?' Vince said.
'Last day of the holidays.'

The mud was black, and slippery, and shiny.
It smelled a lot too.
We jumped in
And ran across the Flats.
There, and back again.
We got covered in mud.

It was great.

When I went in for my tea
Mum didn't say anything.
She just opened her mouth.
And closed it again.
And went kind of red.

'It clears the old head,' I said
And laughed.

And she sent me to bed!

Jenny Sinclair

Devotion

Ginny darling
Lambie pie
Love you
Till
The day
I
Die.

If you ask
The reason
Why
It's because
You are
My
Ginny darling
Lambie pie.

Anon

Gloria

Inside, as the sky darkens and
The rain lashes on windows,
Gloria sits on brightly-coloured cushions,
Gurgling and laughing
Among books, paints and flowers,
And her smile lights up the room.

Tom Edwards

Inconsiderate Hannah

Naughty little Hannah said
  She could make her Grandma whistle;
So, that night, inside her bed
Placed some nettles and a thistle.

Though dear Grandma quite infirm is,
  Heartless Hannah watched her settle
With her poor old epidermis
Resting up against a nettle.

Suddenly she reached the thistle!
  My! You should have heard her whistle!

A successful plan was Hannah's,
But I cannot praise her manners.

D. Streamer (1899)

Harry the hawk

Harry the Hawk on his magic trapeze
Flies over the roofs of the city with ease.
He hangs by his heels and he swings by his knees.
Tumultuous Harry the Hawk.

He has the grand acrobatical style.
Stop when you see him and watch for a while.
He has a secret tucked into his smile.
Mysterious Harry the Hawk.

If he should fall, there's no need for dismay,
He'll just give a laugh that is gallant and gay.
Spreading his wings, he'll go floating away.
That's why he's Harry the Hawk,

Bird boy with never a fret or a care,
Woven of sunshine and warm summer air,
Sparrows and stars in the net of his hair.
Fantastical Harry the Hawk.

Margaret Mahy

Hector the collector

Hector the collector
Collected bits of string,
Collected dolls with broken heads
And rusty bells that would not ring
Pieces out of picture puzzles,
Bent-up nails and ice cream sticks,
Twists of wires, worn-out tyres,
Paper bags and broken bricks,
Old chipped vases, half shoelaces,
Gatlin' guns that wouldn't shoot,
Leaky boots that wouldn't float
And stopped-up horns that wouldn't toot.
Butter knives that had no handles,
Copper keys that fit no locks,
Rings that were too small for fingers,
Dried-up leaves and patched-up socks,
Worn-out belts that had no buckles,
'Lectric trains that had no tracks,
Airplane models, broken bottles,
Three-legged chairs and cups with cracks.
Hector the collector
Loved these things with all his soul –
Loved them more than shining diamonds,
Loved them more than glistenin' gold.
Hector called to all the people,
'Come and share my treasure trunk,'
And all the silly sightless people
Came and looked . . . and called it junk.

Shel Silverstein

Girls and boys, come out to play

Girls and boys, come out to play!
The moon doth shine as bright as day,
So leave your supper and leave your slate,
Susan, Peter and Paul and Kate –
Are you coming?
Head over heels they leapt from bed,
And Tarry Awhile and Sleepyhead
Crept from the bench in the chimney nook.
The children came from the picture books,
Little Jack Horner, Miss Bo-peep –
'Somebody please look after my sheep!' –
Red Riding Hood hot from the wolf in the
    wood,
And baby Helen would come if she could.
(Who's Helen, you ask? Helen's my daughter.
Blue eyes, white hair, she's only a quarter.)
Jack and Jill and Margery Daw,
Miss Muffet, the spider, and Punch and more
Came with a shout, came with a bound
And danced in the moonlight round and round.

What shall we play till break of day,
Mulberry Bush or Nuts and May?
Said the owl in the willow, 'Tuwhit, tuwhoo!
I'm game to hunt the slipper or shoe,'
But as nobody offered a shoe or slipper
They had to do with a breakfast kipper,
Which answered well till it made a mess
Of Miss Muffet's beautiful blue print dress.

O come with a whistle, come with a call,
Come with a will or come not at all!
Who's clattering there? It's Old Mother Hubbard
Playing Grandmother's Footsteps in front of her
   cupboard.
'Any pies?' said Horner. Old Mother said,
   'None!'
But he put in his finger and pulled out a plum.
Up the ladder and down the wall,
A half-penny roll will serve us all:
But Jack rolled right from the top of the hill
And cracked his crown, and so did Jill.

Now for another game – what do you think
Of Hide and Seek or Tiddlywink,
Oranges and Lemons (oh for a taste!)
Or Follow My Leader? – hold on to my waist,
Through moon-white woods we'll twist and
   twine –
Now, Margery Daw, don't break the line.
But Margery stopped to play Pig in the Middle
With the dish and the spoon while the cat played
   the fiddle.
And the tail swept onward, on with a bound
To the windmill, over the river and round,
Till Wee Willie Winkie overhead
As he flew in the sky, in the witch-way, said:
'You children ought to be in bed!'

Girls and boys, go home to rest –
Jenny Wren's asleep in her nest,
The owl has floated back to his willow,
Punch is using his hump as a pillow.
The sleepy children droop and drop,
Unwound as weary spinning top,
And crawl to bed. Miss Bo-peep
(No sheep) is sobbing herself to sleep,
While downstairs huddle into a corner
Miss Muffet, spider, Little Jack Horner.
Open the door, you'll see Mother Hubbard
Curled up like a cat, top shelf in her cupboard.

Lastly, dragging leg on leg,
Tarry Awhile and Sleepyhead,
Dozing, climb the window through,
Stretch and yawn . . . I'm sleepy too
And wonder, in the moonlight gleaming
What is baby Helen dreaming? . . .
   Sssh!
       Don't wake her.
             Good night.

Ian Serraillier

Henry and Mary

Henry was a young king,
  Mary was his queen;
He gave her a snowdrop
  On a stalk of green.

Then all for his kindness
  And all for his care
She gave him a new-laid egg
  In the garden there.

'Love, can you sing?' – 'I cannot sing.'
'Or tell a tale?' – 'Not one I know.'
'Then let us play at queen and king
As down the garden walks we go.'

Anon

White cat

I like to go to the stable after supper –
Remembering fried potatoes and tarts of snow-
    apple jam –
And watch the men curry the horses,
And feed the pigs, and especially give the butting
    calves their milk.
When my father has finished milking he will say,
'Now Howard, you'll have to help me carry in
    these pails.
How will your mother be getting along
All this time without her little man?'
So we go in, and he carries them, but I help.
My father and I don't need the lanterns.
They hang on the wires up high back of the stalls
And we leave them for Ern and Dick.
It seems such a long way to the house in the
    dark,
But sometimes we talk, and always
There's the White Cat, that has been watching
While my father milked.
In the dark its gallop goes before like air,
Without any noise,
And it thinks we're awfully slow
Coming with the milk.

Raymond Kinste

There was a young fellow called Hugh

There was a young fellow called Hugh
Who went to a neighbouring zoo.
  The lion opened wide
  And said, 'Come inside
And bring all the family too.'

Max Fatchen

Ian said

Ian said,
Down behind the dustbin
I met a dog called Sue.
'What are you doing here?' I said.
'I've got nothing else to do.'

Michael Rosen

The sniffle

In spite of her sniffle,
Isabel's chiffle.
Some girls with a sniffle
Would be weepy and tiffle;
They would look awful,
Like a rained-on waffle,
But Isabel's chiffle
In spite of her sniffle.
Her nose is more red
With a cold in her head,
But then, to be sure,
Her eyes are bluer.
Some girls with a sniffle,
Their tempers are uffle,
But when Isabel's snivelly
She's snivelly civilly,
And when she is sniffly
She's perfectly luffly.

Ogden Nash

Jacky

Jacobus, Jacomus, Jaques, Giacomo,
Jaime or Jacob, Hamish, Diego
are only alternative versions of James
and Jacqueline, Jacoba, Jaquetta (names
from which Jacky derives) are the feminine.
So you could say that Jacky is sister to Jim.

But Jackie, applied to a boy, comes from John
(which means God is gracious) and so they go on
with Juan, Giovanni, Ivan and Sean,
Janet or Janice, Jessie and Jane.
So John's brother is Jack, Jacob's sister is Jacky
and both of their names sound friendly and
   happy.

Jane Whittle

Bunches of grapes

'Buches of grapes,' says Timothy;
'Pomegranates pink,' says Elaine;
'A junket of cream and a cranberry tart
   For me,' says Jane.

'Love-in-a-mist,' says Timothy;
'Primroses pale,' says Elaine;
'A nosegay of pinks and mignonette
   For me,' says Jane.

'Chariots of gold,' says Timothy;
'Silvery wings,' says Elaine;
'A bumpity ride in a wagon of hay
   For me,' says Jane.

Walter de la Mare

My sister is missing

Harriet, Harriet, jump in your chariot,
My sister is missing, poor Janet!
And Michael, O Michael, go pedal your cycle,
And search every part of the planet.

My sister, my sister, since breakfast I've missed
    her,
I'll never grow used to the silence;
So Cecil, O Cecil, I'm glad you can wrestle,
For Janet is prone to use violence.

With Doris and Maurice and Horace and Boris
We'll follow the points of the compass,
And if we should find her, we'll creep up behind
    her,
But quietly, for Janet might thump us.

We'll hold her and scold her until we have told
    her
That running away isn't funny;
But if she says sorry, we'll hire a big lorry,
And drive off to somewhere that's sunny.

We'll wander and ponder in fields over yonder,
But wait! What's that dot in the distance?
It looks like a figure, it's getting much bigger,
It's shouting at all my assistants.

O Janet, my Janet, it can't be, or can it?
My sister is no longer missing!
Hooray! We have found her, let's gather around
    her,
Let's start all the hugging and kissing!

Colin West

Cream

Jean, Jean, Jean,
The cat's at the cream,
Supping wi' her forefeet,
And glowering wi' her een!

Anon

Jeff

A young scuba-diver called Jeff
Was so good at holding his breff
He could swim anywhere
On a lungful of air
Which scared his poor muvver to deff.

Michael Palin

The riddling knight

There were three sisters fair and bright,
  Jennifer, Gentle and Rosemary,
And they three loved one valiant knight—
  As the dove flies over the mulberry-tree.

The eldest sister let him in,
And barr'd the door with a silver pin.

The second sister made his bed,
And placed soft pillows under his head.

The youngest sister that same night
Was resolved for to wed wi' this valiant knight.

'And if you can answer questions three,
O then, fair maid, I'll marry wi' thee.

'O what is louder nor a horn,
Or what is sharper nor a thorn?

'Or what is heavier nor the lead,
Or what is better nor the bread?

'Or what is longer nor the way,
Or what is deeper nor the sea?'—

'O shame is louder nor a horn,
And hunger is sharper nor a thorn.

'O sin is heavier nor the lead,
The blessing's better nor the bread.

'O the wind is longer nor the way
And love is deeper nor the sea.'

'You have answer'd aright my questions three',
  Jennifer, Gentle and Rosemary;
'And now, fair maid, I'll marry wi' thee',
  As the dove flies over the mulberry-tree.

Anon

Jenny kissed me

Jenny kissed me when we met,
  Jumping from the chair she sat in;
Time, you thief, who love to get
  Sweets into your list, put that in!
Say I'm weary, say I'm sad,
  Say that health and wealth have missed me,
Say I'm growing old, but add,
  Jenny kissed me.

Leigh Hunt

Jeremy

Didn't do it, wasn't me,
So says little Jeremy,
I was out when that was done,
Didn't touch a single one,
Couldn't have been, wasn't here,
I was out and nowhere near,
Must have fallen off the shelf,
On its own, all by itself,

Shoes aren't muddy, couldn't be,
So says little Jeremy,
Hope you don't think I did that,
All that dirt upon the mat,
Never saw that dirt before,
Didn't put it on the floor,
I've been playing where it's clean,
Was no mud where I have been,

Wasn't my fault, couldn't be,
So says little Jeremy,
They just tore all on their own,
Says the boy in sorrowed tone,
Wasn't playing in the tree,
Couldn't help it, honestly,
Someone must have made me trip,
And it's such a tiny rip,

Why's it me you always blames,
Little Jeremy complains,
Just because I'm still a kid,
Automatically I did,
This time I must make you see,
That it really wasn't me,
Please mum, there's been some mistake,
I never made that window break.

Paul Sayers

Growing pain

The boy was barely five years old.
We sent him to the little school
And left him there to learn the names
Of flowers in jam jars on the sill
And learn to do as he was told.
He seemed quite happy there until
Three weeks afterwards, at night,
The darkness whimpered in his room.
I went upstairs, switched on his light,
And found him wide awake, distraught,
Sheets mangled and his eiderdown
Untidy carpet on the floor.
I said, 'Why can't you sleep? A pain?'
He snuffled, gave a little moan,
And then he spoke a single word:
'Jessica.' The sound was blurred.
'Jessica? What do you mean?'
'A girl at school called Jessica,
She hurts—' he touched himself between
The heart and stomach '—she has been
Aching here and I can see her.'
Nothing I had read or heard
Instructed me in what to do.
I covered him and stroked his head.
'The pain will go, in time,' I said.

Vernon Scannell

Jelly and melons

When Jilly eats jelly,
Then Jilly is jolly.
But melons make Melanie
Most melancholy.

Peter Wesley Smith

Nomenclature

'What terrible names
Are "Jamie" and "James" '
Thought Jim.
' "Peter" is sweeter
And "Patrick" is neater.'

But when he was christened,
Nobody listened
To HIM.

Colin West

Joan who hates parties

Today's little Doreen's party-day;
And it all begins when I'm snatched from play
By Mother, who cries with a gay little laugh,
'Now come along first and have a nice bath!'
And off come my jeans and I'm dumped straight
   in,
And splashed all over from toes to chin;
Then dumped out again on the big bath-mat –
And don't I just hate that!

For the next half-hour I am rubbed rough-dry,
And tickled with talc till I'm ready to cry,
And perched half-dressed on a backless chair
For the fight between Mother and me and my
   hair;
Then on go the shoes and the clean white socks,
And the dreamiest of dream-like nylon frocks,
With a sweet blue bow for the end of my plait –
And don't I just hate that!

But I'm ready at last; and at ten-past four
I'll be dropped at dear little Doreen's door;
And at Doreen's door I'll be met with a hearty
Welcome to dear little Doreen's party;
But they won't see me – they won't see Joan –
But a girl with a heart like a thunder-stone;
A girl with the face of a fierce tom-cat . . .
And won't they just hate that!

John Walsh

Joe

I say:
What are you doing? And our little boy Joe says
Mm?
What d'you think you're doing?
Mm?
Why did you do that?
Mm?
The peanut butter. All over your blanket.
Mm?
And the talcum powder?
Mm?
Don't do it – do you understand?
Mm?
Or there'll be trouble. And Joe says,
Trouble,
and runs off laughing.

Michael Rosen

Little John was not content

Little John was not content
Unless he played with wet cement.
  One day alas in someone's yard,
  He stayed too long and set quite hard.
His mother didn't want him home
So now he's just a garden gnome.

Max Fatchen

Mischief

Teacher, teacher come and see
Johnny only hitting me
Terry pinching Nita hand
Jimmy shooting rubber-band.

Odette Thomas

Infant Joy

(Innocence)

'I have no name:
I am but two days old.'
What shall I call thee?
'I happy am,
Joy is my name.'
Sweet joy befall thee!

Pretty Joy!
Sweet Joy, but two days old!
Sweet Joy I call thee.
Thou dost smile,
I sing the while,
Sweet joy befall thee!

William Blake

Blame

Graham, look at Maureen's leg,
She says you tried to tattoo it!
I did, Miss, yes – with my biro,
But Jonathan told me to do it.

Graham, look at Peter's sock,
It's got a burn-hole through it!
It was just an experiment, Miss, with the lens.
Jonathan told me to do it.

Alice's bag is stuck to the floor,
Look, Graham, did you glue it?
Yes, but I never thought it would work,
And Jonathan told me to do it.

Jonathan, what's all this I hear
About you and Graham Prewitt?
Well, Miss it's really more his fault:
He *tells* me to tell him to do it!

Allan Ahlberg

Lemon squash

Joshua, Joshua,
Why don't you call and see Mama?
She'll be pleased to know
That you're my best beau.
Joshua, Joshua,
Sweeter than lemon squash you are,
Yes, by Gosh you are!
Josh -U-Osh-U-R.

(Popular song)

Justin

'Just in a minute,' said Justin
'Just in a moment,' he said
'Just let me choose which tie I'm to wear'
Justin tried on the blue, then the red

'Justin, we're waiting,' said Mother
'Justin, we're angry,' said Dad
Justin came down adjusting his tie
'Just in time, Justin, my lad.'

Tom Edwards

Katherine Tattles

When Kate and Karen
Have their battles,
Katherine tattles.

When Kay and Katherine
Have a spat,
Kate tells that.

When Katherine and Kate
Their tempers lose,
Kay spreads the news.

But Karen gets
The greatest glory.
She turns a friendly fight
Into a full-length story,
And makes it gory.

Leland B. Jacobs

Marbles

Jacks, snowys and squids
Spiders with traps
Frogs eyes and rainbow jacks
Milkshakes and lits
But best are king bigs!

Galaxies – big ones –
Bullies make tricks
Rainbow holly sparkles
So do snowy lits!

Kevin's got marbles
Play you a squid?
Squid for two bigs?
Isn't worth it!

Sarah Edenbrow (aged 8)

A garden of girls

Kate is like a violet, Gertrude's like a rose,
Jane is like a gillyflower smart;
But Laura's like a lily, the purest bud that blows,
Whose white, white petals veil the golden heart.
Girls in the garden – one and two and three –
One for song and one for play and one – ah,
 one for me!
Gillyflowers and violets and roses fair and fine,
But only one a lily, and that one lily mine!

Bertha is a hollyhock, stately, tall, and fair,
Mabel has the daisy's dainty grace,
Edith has the gold of the sunflower on her hair,
But Laura wears the lily in her face.
Girls in the garden – five and six and seven;
Three to take, and three to give, but one – ah!
 one is given;
Hollyhocks and daisies, and sunflowers like the
 sun,
But only one a lily, and one lily won.

E. Nesbit

Haiku

Lee chatting away.
Miss Crawford says, 'Quietly!'
I say, 'Quiet, Lee.'

Anon

The last word of a bluebird

as told to a child

As I went out a Crow
In a low voice said, 'Oh,
I was looking for you.
How do you do?
I just came to tell you
To tell Lesley (will you?)
That her little Bluebird
Wanted me to bring word
That the north wind last night
That made the stars bright
And made ice on the trough
Almost made him cough
His tail feathers off.
He just had to fly!
But he sent her Good-bye,
And said to be good,
And wear her red hood,
And look for skunk tracks
In the snow with an axe –
And do everything!
And perhaps in the spring
He would come back and sing.'

Robert Frost

Lewis has a trumpet

A trumpet
A trumpet
Lewis has a trumpet
A bright one that's yellow
A loud proud horn.
He blows it in the evening
When the moon is newly rising
He blows it when it's raining
In the cold and misty morn
It honks and it whistles
It roars like a lion
It rumbles like a lion
With a wheezy huffing hum
His parents say it's awful
Oh really simply awful
But
Lewis says he loves it
It's such a handsome trumpet
And when he's through with trumpets
He's going to buy a drum.

Karla Kuskin

From Linda

Linda, Linda, slender and pretty,
Biscuit girl in a biscuit city,
Packing the biscuits in paper boxes,
What do you dream of? How do you dream?
The cutters rise and fall and rise and cut
The chocolate, the coconut,
The Orange Princess and the Gypsy Cream.
The biscuits gather and the boxes shut,
But things are never what they seem.

In the school the bells are ringing,
In the playground girls are singing:
  (Lily, paper, hard-boiled eggs,
  Mr Swain has bandy legs.)
Linda, Linda, rude and sweet
Skipping girl in a skipping street,
Singing and skipping all summer long:
    (Worms in the classroom, worms in the hall,
    Mr Swain will eat them all.)

The cutters fall and rise and fall
And biscuits are unending like a wall
And school is over and the summer's dream.

John Fuller

Night

Lisa, Lisa
Raise your head,
The moon is shining on your bed

Lisa, Lisa
Hear the shiver,
Hangers in the wardrobe quiver

Lisa, Lisa
Stretch your arm,
Feel the darkness with your palm

Lisa, Lisa
Taste and smell
The dust that fills the air as well

Lisa, Lisa
As you sleep
And from your mind your senses creep,
Does the outside world go on,
Or has the dust, the darkness gone?

Emma Payne

The Christening

– Name this child –

LOUISE they name you.
Child not mine, but of my blood.
Child of my child, so double loved.

– Look upon this child –

And what for you, if I could choose?
What gifts across the years?
What faery gold to keep you strong,
Protect you from our fears?

– Grant to this child –

A tranquil heart, contented mind,
A spirit brave and rare,
Compassion, kindness, joy and love,
Capacity to care.

– Bless this child –

But more than these,
Yes, more than all,
To make your whole life true –
No matter what THEY do or say,
The courage to be YOU.

– Receive this child –

Jenny Craig

The lost shoe

Poor little Lucy
By some mischance,
Lost her shoe
As she did dance:
'Twas not on the stairs,
Not in the hall;
Not where they sat
At supper at all.
She looked in the garden,
But there it was not;
Henhouse, or kennel,
Or high dovecote.
Dairy and meadow,
And wild woods through
Showed not a trace
Of Lucy's shoe.
Bird nor bunny
Nor glimmering moon
Breathed a whisper
Of where 'twas gone.
It was cried and cried,
Oyez and Oyez!

In French, Dutch, Latin,
And Portuguese.
Ships the dark seas
Went plunging through,
But none brought news
Of Lucy's shoe;
And still she patters
In silk and leather,
O'er snow, sand, shingle,
In every weather;
Spain, and Africa,
Hindustan,
Java, China,
And lamped Japan;
Plain and desert,
She hops – hops through,
Pernambuco
To gold Peru;
Mountain and forest,
And river too,
All the world over
For her lost shoe.

Walder de la Mare

Luke

Luke's a lisper.
I've heard a whisper,
He's at his zenith
Playing tennith.

Colin West

Lynne

There was a young lady called Lynne
Who was so uncommonly thin
That when she essayed
To drink lemonade
She slipped down the straw and fell in.

Anon

Mandy likes the mud

Polly likes to play with toys
Melissa makes a lot of noise
Ann has a bike
Trevor a trike
But Mandy likes the mud.
She jumps in it
She slumps in it
She scoops it in her hands
She rides on it
She slides on it
She digs to foreign lands.

Kevan likes to kick a ball
Peter never plays at all
Tina cooks tarts
Donna plays darts
But Mandy loves the mud.
She galumphs in it
She splarges
She glugs and slurps and slops
She grins in it
She swims in it
She does smacking belly flops.

Tricia talks to her teddy bear
Belinda combs her doll's long hair
Tracy plays tennis
Mark is a menace
But Mandy adores the mud.
She dives in it
She thrives in it
She paints it on the wall
She goes splash in it
She goes splosh in it
She does the breast stroke and the crawl.

Ronnie likes falling
And snowballing in snow
Lucy is learning how to row
Louise loves a sing-song
Paula likes ping-pong
But Mandy rejoices in mud.
She has sat in it
Filled her hat with it
She washed the neighbour's cat in it
She hid from Mum in it
Banged her drum in it
She fell down on her bum in it.

Kenneth kicks an old tin can
Anthony plays with his Action Man
Wanda is waiting
For Sam to go skating
But Mandy lives in the mud.
So if you're looking for Mandy
Find the muddiest mess
At Mud House, Mud Corner
Her permanent address.

Gareth Owen

Millions of Strawberries

Marcia and I went over the curve
Eating our way down
Jewels of strawberries we didn't deserve.
Eating our way down.
Till our hands were sticky, and our lips painted.
And over us the hot day fainted,
And we saw snakes,
And got scratched,
And a lust overcame us for the red unmatched
Small buds of berries,
Till we lay down –
Eating our way down –
And rolled in the berries like two little dogs.
Rolled
in the late gold.
And gnats hummed,
And it was cold,
And home we went, home without a berry,
Painted red and brown,
Eating our way down.

Genevieve Taggard

Acrostic

Maidens, if a maid you meet
Always free from pout and pet,
Ready smile and temper sweet,
Greet my little Margaret.
And if loved by all she be
Rightly, not a pampered pet,
Easily you then may see
'Tis my little Margaret.

Lewis Carroll

Maria's purse

Maria had an aunt at Leeds,
For whom she made a purse of beads;
'Twas neatly done, by all allow'd,
And praise soon made her vain and proud.

Her mother, willing to repress
This strong conceit of cleverness,
Said: 'I will show you, if you please,
A Honeycomb, the work of Bees!

'Yes, look within their hive, and then
Examine well your purse again;
Compare your merits, and you will
Admit the Insects' greater skill!'

Elizabeth Turner (c. 1800)

Football

I must wash the dishes for Mum.
I know that,
But the kitchen is full of the shouting of my
football team's supporters.
Crowds and crowds
Arm to arm,
Shoulder to shoulder,
Colours in scarves, hats, cheeks, jerseys
Screaming at each other over the pitch
Louder sometimes than the hullaballoo of the
    crowd.
All this I see in the mountain of bubbles.

'It's a goal!' I yell
And throw the dish-cloth in the air.
Come on Martin,
Let's leave the rest of the dishes –
You come with me,
Time we got in that crowd!

Melvyn Pressdee

New shoes

Walking proudly along the road
in my new clothes.
Oh!
But not forgetting the shoes,
and I mean not forgetting the shoes.
They were new also.
But
every time I took a step
the heel dug painfully into the back of my foot.
Then all of a sudden
'Michelle, you do look smart! Is there anything
    wrong?'
'Oh no, of course there isn't' I answered
walking with a limp.
Then came another voice.
'Michelle, I just love those shoes!
Where did you get them?'
As I entered into a long chat with my new friend
I thought,
'These shoes ain't bad after all,
cos at least somebody likes them,
even if I don't.'

Michelle Campbell

Next year

Next year Matt and I'll go back
  To fields and cooling streams,
To sticks and mud and hot, hot sun,
  And half-forgotten dreams.

We built our hideouts in the woods
  They'll still be there, the same,
We'll be the pirate castaways
  In some bewitching game.

Next year we'll stay for longer
  And finish all our plays,
We'll stay as long as summers last,
  For days, and days, and days.

Rosemary Cowan

My Uncle Ronnie

My uncle Ronnie
took me to Hackney Downs
and said:
how's your eyes?
how far can you see with your eyes?

So I said:
I can see that tree over there.
so he said:
Aha. But can you see the leaves on the tree over
    there?
and I said:
I can see that tree
I can see the leaves
on that tree over there.

All right, he says,
you say you can see the leaves on that tree.
Now, Mick, I'm telling you true
I can see a fly
sitting on a leaf
in that tree.
How about you?

And I said:
I don't know.
I'm not sure.
Perhaps.
Maybe.
Sort of.
Nearly.

Now, says my uncle Ron,
you see that tree
you see those leaves
you see that fly
well I tell you
I can see a leg
on that fly
on the leaf
on that tree over there
and what's more –
I can see a hair
on the leg of that fly
on the leaf on that tree over there
and –
Ronnie, I said, Uncle Ron
I can't see the hair on the leg
Uncle Ron, *I* can't see where the hair is.

The hair's on the knee, Mick
the hair's on the knee
Quick, look. Just there, quick.
Oh bad luck. You're too late.
The feller's gone and gone.

Michael Rosen

From Tarantella

Do you remember an Inn,
Miranda?
Do you remember an Inn?
And the tedding and the spreading
Of the straw for a bedding,
And the fleas that tease in the High Pyrenees,
And the wine that tasted of the tar?
And the cheers and the jeers of the young
   muleteers
(Under the dark of the vine verandah)?
Do you remember an Inn, Miranda,
Do you remember an Inn?
And the cheers and the jeers of the young
   muleteers
Who hadn't got a penny,
And who weren't paying any,
And the hammer at the doors
   and the Din?

And the Hip! Hop! Hap!
Of the clap
Of the hands to the twirl and the swirl
Of the girl gone chancing,
Glancing,
Dancing,
Backing and advancing,
Snapping of the clapper to the spin
Out and in—
And the Ting, Tong, Tang of the Guitar!
Do you remember an Inn,
Miranda?
Do you remember an Inn?

Hilaire Belloc

Natalie

It isn't normal, Natalie,
Although you do it daily.
You dress up very tattily
And play the ukelele.

Yet once you dressed so nattily,
Oh Natalie, it's true.
Yes, once you dressed so nattily,
But now you never do.

Colin West

Sad story

There was a young schoolboy called Neal
Who decided to ride on a seal.
He would have survived
If the seal hadn't dived
And the whale hadn't wanted a meal.

Anon

Nicholas Ned

Nicholas Ned,
He lost his head,
And put a turnip on instead;
But then, ah me!
He could not see,
So he thought it was night, and he went to bed.

Laura Richards

The production line

Nick paints the outside
Stan paints the inside
They do it all through the day
Tom does the nuts up
Bill does the bolts up
They always do it that way
Alf puts the wheels on
Bert puts the tyres on
They fix 'em so they're OK
Ted puts the engine
Arthur puts the boot in

But Fred's ill and he's not here today
Len puts the front seat in
George puts the back seat in
They fix 'em so they'll stay
Dan puts the lights on
Henry puts the bumpers on
Waiting for a tea break so they can get away
John puts the steering wheels in
Charlie puts the key in
And drives the car away
They can't stop long
Because as soon as that one's gone
There's another one on the way

Bobby Pearce (aged 14)

Nicola

I'm glad I'm not
Like Nicola,
Who may look sweet
As honey,
But even if you
Tickle her,
She doesn't find
It funny.

Colin West

Lost love

Nigel and Julie were sweethearts
They'd walk home from school hand in hand
Ignoring the wolf whistles, cat-calls and jokes
They lived in their own fairyland.

But their school work soon started to suffer
Julie's Mum despaired, 'Where will it end?
My daughter's stopped eating, stopped talking,
    stopped sleeping
It's driving me right round the bend!'

Now Nigel's Dad, Keith, was an airman
One day he was told to change base,
Nigel telephoned Julie and whispered 'We're
    through'
So she fell for Prince Charles in his place.

Louise Draycott

Lunar Oona

There was a young lady called Oona
Whose passions were perfectly lunar.
She flew to the moon
For the whole month of June,
And wished she had landed there sunar.

Anon

Owen

There was a young fellow called Owen
Who had to keep goin' and goin'.
Psychiatrists said
Being dropped on his head
Had caused all the toin' and froin'.

Michael Palin

Penny

There was a young lady called Penny
Whose hobbies and interests were many
But the thing she liked most –
As she'd boast coast-to-coast –
Was tap-dancing at Abergavenny

Louise Draycott

Peter and Michael

Peter and Michael were two little menikin,
They kept a cock and a fat little henikin:
Instead of an egg it laid a gold penikin,
Oh, how they wish it would do it againikin!

Anon

The story of Fidgety Philip

One evening Philip's father said,
'You twist and squirm and shake your head.
Come, let us see if you are able
To sit quite still for once at table.'
But not a word
Had Philip heard.
He giggled
And wiggled
And wriggled
And tottered
And teetered
And rocked in his chair.
Till his father cried, 'Philip!
Sit still – or beware!'

Caring nothing for disaster,
Backwards, forwards, always faster,
Philip rocked – until the chair
Slipped from under. Then and there
Philip grabbed the table cloth,
Spilling everything: the broth,
Bread and butter, all the dishes,
Goblets, gravy, meat and fishes,
Cauliflower, garden greens,
Spinach, parsnips, peas and beans,
Pastry, puddings white and brown . . .
Everything came tumbling down!

———

Meanwhile where was Philip? There,
Underneath the ruined chair,
Underneath – as you might guess –
Broken plates, a horrid mess,
Groaning, in a hideous mood,
Soaked from head to toe with food.
And, to make his plight complete,
Nothing left for him to eat!

Heinrich Hoffman

Phoebe

A certain young chap named Bill Beebee
Was in love with a lady named Phoebe.
   'But,' said he, 'I must see
   What the licence fee be
Before Phoebe be Phoebe B. Beebee.'

Anon

Pippa's song

(From Pippa Passes)

The year's at the spring
And day's at the morn;
Morning's at seven;
The hill-side's dew-pearled;
The lark's on the wing;
The snail's on the thorn:
God's in His heaven –
All''s right with the world!

Robert Browning

Polly, Dolly, Kate and Molly

Polly, Dolly, Kate and Molly,
All are filled with pride and folly.
   Polly tattles,
   Dolly wriggles,
   Katy rattles,
   Molly giggles;
Whoever knew such constant rattling,
Wriggling, giggling, noise, and tattling.

Anon

Queenie

Queenie, Queenie, on the wall,
Who has got the golden ball?

Is she fat or is she thin?
Does she play the violin?

I haven't got it,
It isn't in my pocket.

Queenie, Queenie, sitting on the wall,
Tell me, tell me, who's got the ball?

(Playground ball game)

From The wicked children's alphabet

Quentin was a quiet child
To all he seemed quite meek and mild.
He could knit and crochet things
Like complicated insects' wings.

Rhoda, who preferred to run
Freely in the summer sun,
Thought he was a boring lad –
And the 'softest' friend she had.

So she called him 'Little Quilt'.
Then a lot of blood was spilt!

Pauline Mitchell

Rebecca

Who slammed Doors for Fun and Perished Miserably

A Trick that everyone abhors
In Little Girls is slamming Doors.
A Wealthy Banker's Little Daughter
Who lived in Palace Green, Bayswater
(By name Rebecca Offendort),
Was given to this Furious Sport.

She would deliberately go
And Slam the door like Billy-Ho!
To make her Uncle Jacob start.
She was not really bad at heart,
But only rather rude and wild;
She was an aggravating child.

It happened that a Marble Bust
Of Abraham was standing just
Above the Door this little Lamb
Had carefully prepared to Slam,
And Down it came! It knocked her flat!
It laid her out! She looked like that!

Her Funeral Sermon (which was long
And followed by a Sacred Song)
Mentioned her Virtues, it is true,
But dwelt upon her Vices, too,
And showed the Dreadful End of One
Who goes and slams the Door for Fun.

Hilaire Belloc

Richard's brother speaks

Richard . . . .
What's the matter? Why you not smilin' no more?
You wretch, you bruk the window?
Daddy a go peel you 'kin,
'im a go peel it like how he peel orange.
When Daddy come true dat door
You better run.
You better leave de country!
'im a-go peel you 'kin.
You bottom a go warm tonight though!
Me goin' cook dinner pon you backside
When 'im done wid you
Richard 'im a come!
Run, bwoy, run!

Desmond Strachan

The story of flying Robert

When the rain comes tumbling down
In the country or the town
All good little girls and boys
Stay at home and mind their toys.

Robert thought, 'No, when it pours
It is better out of doors.'
Rain it *did*, and in a minute
Bob was in it.

What a wind! Oh! how it whistles
Through the trees and flowers and thistles!
It has caught his red umbrella;
Now look at him, silly fellow.

Up he flies
To the skies.
No one heard his screams and cries,
Through the clouds the rude wind bore him,
And his hat flew on before him.
Soon they got to such a height
They were nearly out of sight!
And the hat went up so high,
That it really touched the sky.
No one even yet could tell
Where they slipp'd, or where they fell.
Only, this one thing is plain,
Bob was never seen again!

Heinrich Hoffmann

Robin and Richard

Up in the green orchard there is a green tree,
The finest of pippins that you may see;
The apples are ripe, and ready to fall,
And Robin and Richard shall gather them all.

(Nursery rhyme)

Problem child

How *shall* I deal with Roger, Mrs Prodger?
I've never yet been able
To sit him at a table
And make him paint a label
For the salmon in the kindergarten shop.
   But he's full of animation
   When I mention a dictation,
   And he never wants a spelling-test to stop.
I've encouraged self-expression
And intentional digression
But I think I'll have to let the system drop.
   For the normal child, like Roger,
   Is a *do*-er, not a dodger,
And your methods, Mrs Prodger, are a flop.

How *shall* I deal with Roger, Mrs Prodger?
I've had projects on the fairies,
On markets, shops and dairies;
I've had projects on the *prairies*,
But the little fellow doesn't want to play:
   Instead he has a yearning
   For unreasonable learning,
   And wants to do Arithmetic all day.
He shows a strong proclivity
For purposeful activity,
And doesn't want experience in clay.
   So I rather think that Roger
   Is a *do-*er, not a dodger,
And how *would* you deal with Roger, can you
   say?

J. E. Faulks

Here's a story

Here's a story
Of my friend Rory.
He fell off the wall –
And that's all!

Anon

A pair of slippers

Sleeping in the big bed
   Rosamund; and, below,
An empty pair of slippers,
   Just where slippers go.

Very very quiet,
   And very very neat:
Anyone would *know* they came
   Off a good girl's feet.

Just a little lonely,
   Just a little sad,
Out upon the cold floor –
   Oh, anything but bad!

Never was a pair of
   Shoes so good as they –
But oh, the dance they'll lead her
   All the bouncing day!

E. V. Rieu

Nothing, that's what

'What *are* you doing, Rupert?'
There comes the same reply,
For Rupert answers, 'Nothing.'
And that's his daily cry.

'What are you DOING, Rupert?
Who broke the garden pot?'
But Rupert answers, 'Nothing.'
And nothing's not a lot.

Whenever people blame him
For doing such-and-such
Then Rupert's doing nothing,
Which isn't very much.

'We want to SEE you, Rupert,
Who made this awful mess?'
But Rupert's doing nothing.
Well, nothing more or less.

And so we have this problem
To puzzle anyone,
How Rupert's doing nothing,
Yet naughty things get done.

Max Fatchen

Sally won't you walk with me?

'Sally won't you walk with me
Walking heel and toe
Sally can we secrets share
As home from school we go.'

Arm in arm by lane and hedge
So many tales to tell
And every tale breeds tales anew
As we walk in a magic spell.

'And do you know what Brenda said
And how Alan banged his head
How Antonia cried at dinner time
And what Jemima said?'

'And wasn't dinner awful?
And Sally tell your dream
And will you come to tea next week?
And isn't Rose a scream?'

'Did you really tell your mother that
Did your sister cut your hair
Did you see that lady on the bike
Did you see those two boys stare?'

'And Sally look, stop giggling
Oh Sally honestly
Oh Sally don't you pull that face
Those people there will see.'

'What did your father say to that
And did you do it again?
You didn't really, I don't believe!
Sally what happened then?'

We whisper over Sally's gate
Till her mother calls her to tea
So many secrets still to tell
So many tales about me.

And if I could wish my days again
If time were a golden spool
I'd wish I could walk for ever
With Sally home from school.

Gareth Owen

Sam

Sam is my name.
I am Sam.
I am the same
Sam, I am.

As I sit here
in my pram
my career
is being Sam.

Jane Whittle

Sister Sandy

Hippity hop to the barber shop
To buy a stick of candy;
One for me and one for you
And one for sister Sandy.

(Ball bouncing rhyme)

Sarah sang

In the summer Sarah sang
On the train
On the beach
In the sea
On a boat
At the fair
In the fields
Even when she was asleep
Sarah sang

But in the winter Sarah sniffed
On the bus
In the classroom
In the playground
In the rain
On the ice
In the snow
Even when she sang
Sarah sniffed

Tom Edwards

Shannon

Shannon isn't beautiful,
Not in the usual way,
Would never win Miss Pears contest –
Unless *I* had final say!
Has a pointed, pixie face,
She doesn't often laugh,
But her black eyes shine and sparkle
When you go to run her bath.

She used to be so quiet
But she's found her voice at last,
Assisted by the kind of toys
That deafen with a blast.
She hoards her precious booty
But it rarely ends up broken.
Ask her to return it –
It's as if you'd never spoken.

She can be a little darling
She can be a little witch,
But when she weaves her spell on me
I know that I am rich.

Suzanne Yorke

Sharon's life

My name is Sharon
I have two brothers
Called Phillip and William
Sometimes they bother me
But often they don't.
Being me is fun.
When it is older
It won't be so good I think.
Phillip lost my book
It had pictures
He lost it
But I am not very cross.
Daddy bought it.
Aunt Judy died last week
Mummy said it was a loss
And then she cried
Quite a bit.
My dog is called Spot
He has some bad habits.
Perhaps I will find the book.
My bed is green.
I'm five.
That's all.
I'm glad I'm alive.

Gareth Owen

Shirley said

Who wrote 'kick me' on my back?
Who put a spider in my mack?
Who's the one who pulls my hair?
Tries to trip me everywhere?
Who runs up to me and strikes me?
That boy there – I think he likes me.

Dennis Doyle

Boy in bubbles

At the family picnic Dad
shook out the tablecloth, Mum
took out the sandwiches, Gran
opened the thermos flask, Uncle
told a rude joke, Cousin
told a ruder one, Uncle
smacked him, Cousin
wailed, Gran
covered her ears, Mum
ate the sandwiches, Dad said

Where's Simon?

A river runs behind the trees
Where the water licks the stone
As the leaves fly out on smoky froth
And the cold bites to the bone

Here, below the blackened weeds,
Beside the bending tree,
Among the crazed and churning foam
A boy dives: he swims, is free

Emma Payne

For Sophie

Sophie's sleeping,
   Pretty creature,
Yet no wrinkle
   Clouds her features.

Bright eyes shining
   Danced through light,
Drifting, closing
   Into night.

Happy still
   Nor tired of play,
But dark has come
   So, darling, sleep.

Rosemary Cowan

Birthday

It's my birthday today,
And I'm nine.
I'm having a party tonight,
And we'll play on the lawn
If it's fine.
There'll be John, Dick and Jim,
And Alan and Tim,
And Dennis and Brian and Hugh;
But the star of the show,
You'll be sorry to know,
Will be Sue,
(She's my sister, aged two,
And she'll yell till she's blue
In the face, and be sick.)

Anon

Caribbean song rhyme

Stevie pelting Ma Rose mango
With his good friend Hicks
Even though his mother tell him
He would get some licks

Stevie pick up a big boulder
And he aim with zest
What he thought was Julie mango
Was a big jap nest.

The japs start swarming Stevie head
And he start to squeal
His mother said, 'I tried to tell you
Who don't hear does feel.'

Odette Thomas

jap – a wasp
licks – a spanking

The garden girl

Oh Tammy, you're a bonny 'un,
Got a face like a pink chrysanthemum,
Got a nose like a rhododend-e-ron,
And ears like sweet peas.

Anon

Teresa nude

Teresa bathing, glancing down, said 'Mummy,
I wonder what it looks like in my tummy.'

The answer; pictures in a range of inks
From deepest scarlet to indifferent pinks,

– Though possibly the liver, some would deem
Being purplish brown, outside this colour
    scheme.

And pale the bowels' wrinkled furbelows,
Packaged as neatly as a brand-new hose.

Though in the 'tummy' scarcely to be placed,
The fiery lung-trees grow up from the waist.

And a few miscellaneous parts propel
Juices and dinners through the hues of hell.

Teresa, thanks for acting as our guide
To all the beauteous sights we have inside.

Yet better we should merely show our skin,
Be made not inside out but inside in –

For how could we be ever calmly viewed
If the above were what we looked like in the
    nude?

Roy Fuller

More thoughts from a little boy

'No tuck for Toby on Friday,
If he has a moan and a cry day.'
That's what they normally say as a rule,
When I'm sent upstairs to get ready for school.

When you've just started school,
It's a bit of a cheek
To want you to behave
Every day of the week.
I've lost one of my shoes
And I can't find my tie.
'Sno wonder I have a bit of a cry.
I could nip down the stairs,
Grab my coat and my cap and . . .
Walk out of the house as if nothing has
    happened!
They might not notice
And, with any luck,
They'll give me my money – so I can buy tuck!
Oh, there's Mum on the stairs . . .
I'll never get by.
Oh goody! She's found my shoe and my tie.
'Now come along, Toby, and let's get you
    dressed.
We want you to leave home looking your best.
And because you've been helpful and quiet when
    you play,
Here's 10p to spend as it's tuck day today.'

don't think I'll spend it.
Well, perhaps I'll spend some,
But I'll save all the rest, and buy something for
    Mum.

Rod Hull

Tom's little dog

Tom told his dog called Tim to beg,
And up at once he sat,
His two clear amber eyes fixed fast,
His haunches on his mat.

Tom poised a lump of sugar on
His nose; then, 'Trust!' says he;
Stiff as a guardsman sat his Tim;
Never a hair stirred he.

'Paid for!' says Tom; and in a trice
Up jerked that moist black nose;
A snap of teeth, a crunch, a munch,
And down the sugar goes!

Walter de la Mare

Tony O

Over the bleak and barren snow
A voice there came a-calling;
'Where are you going to, Tony O!
Where are you going this morning?'

'I am going where there are rivers of wine,
The mountains bread and honey;
There Kings and Queens do mind the swine,
And the poor have all the money.'

Colin Francis

Embrionic mega-stars

We can play reggae music, funk and skiffle too,
We prefer heavy metal but the classics sometimes
   do.
We're keen on Tamla-Motown, folk and soul,
But most of all, what we like
Is basic rock and roll.
We can play the monochord, the heptachord and
   flute,
We're OK on the saxaphone and think the
   glockenspiel is cute,
We really love the tuba, the balalaika and guitar
And our duets on the clavichord are bound to
   take us far.
We think castanets are smashing, harmonicas are
   fun,
And with the ocarina have only just begun.

We've mastered synthesizers, bassoons and violins
As well as hurdy-gurdies, pan-pipes and
  mandolins.
The tom-tom and the tabor, the trumpet and the
  drum
We learnt to play in between the tintinnabulum.
We want to form a pop group
And will when we're eleven,
But at the moment Tracey's eight
And I am only seven.

Brian Patten

Classics

Ulysses and Jason
Were going to the game
Wrapped in scarves and woollen hats
The colours all the same
The top of the bus was empty
They were the only two
My name's better'n yours,' said Jason
No it ain't,' said U..

Jason was a hero,'
Said Jason, chewing gum,
He went off to find the fleece
With the help of Medea's mum
His ship was called the Argo
The Argonauts they were her crew
My name's better'n yours,' said Jason
No it ain't,' said U.

'Ulysses was the geezer,'
Said Ulie, 'Here are the facts
He beat the Cyclops and ignored the Sirens
By stuffing his ears full of wax
Homer wrote a book on 'im
We've got it in the loo.'
'My name's better'n yours,' said Jason
'No it ain't,' said U.

Benjamin Bolt

Clap-clap clappity clap

Ursula, Ursula, dance with me,
Over the water and over the sea.
    Clap-clap, clappity clap.

Oliver, Oliver, laugh with me,
Over the water and over the sea.
    Clap-clap, clappity clap.

Caroline, Caroline, sing with me,
Over the water and over the sea.
    Clap-clap, clappity clap.

Rachel, Rachel, talk with me,
Over the water and over the sea.
    Clap-clap, clappity clap.

Toni, Toni, write to me,
Over the water and over the sea.
    Clap-clap, clappity clap.

Bridget, Bridget, walk with me,
Over the water and over the sea.
    Clap-clap, clappity clap.

Eleanor, Eleanor, play with me,
Over the water and over the sea.
    Clap-clap, clappity clap.

Daniel, Daniel, read with me,
Over the water and over the sea.
    Clap-clap, clappity clap.

Joanna, Joanna, dream with me,
Over the water and over the sea.
    Clap-clap, clappity clap.

Naomi, Naomi, hop with me,
Over the water and over the sea.
    Clap-clap, clappity clap.

Stephanie, Stephanie, stroll with me,
Over the water and over the sea.
    Clap-clap, clappity clap.

Children all, wherever you may be,
Over the water and over the sea,
    Clap-clap, clappity clap,
Come in a circle, clap with me,
Over the water and over the sea.
    Clap-clap, clappity clap.

(Circular action/clapping song)

Veronica

Now this is a tale of a child I once knew;
Her hair it was golden, her eyes they were blue.
She was sweet, she was kind, she was neat, she
    was fun,
That child she was perfect in all ways but one.
Just that thing about her they all seemed to hate:
If only Veronica wasn't so *late*.

Just getting her up was a terrible fuss.
So late for her breakfast and late for the bus,
And late for her lessons and late for the teams,
I'm certain she must have been late for her
    dreams.
Her programme, which should have been
    tranquil and calm
Was sullied by scuttlings and cries of alarm.
By the dropping of books and the slamming of
    doors,
By the grabbing of coats and by 'No time for
    more!'s.

Veronica's uncle was jolly old Jack.
From the ends of the earth he came hurrying
    back.
His jokes and his hugs and his laughing brown
    eyes
Were welcomed by all with the gladdest of cries,
And when they complained just how late she
    had been
He suggested at once that he wrote to the
    Queen.

'Her Majesty?'
'Yes, at old Buckingham P. Just hand me that
      pen
And then leave it to me.'
Next day when Veronica opened her door
A small woolly puppy sat there on the floor.
He wagged his black tail and he cocked his black
      head,
And looked just exactly as if he had said,
'I'm curly and cuddly and clever and clean,
And proud to be specially sent by the Queen!'

'Twas soon after dawn that he jumped on her
      bed
And woke her by nuzzling the top of her head.
Veronica simply amazed all of them
By coming to breakfast at seven a.m.!
This small woolly puppy which snapped at her
      heels
Delivered her promptly at school and at meals,

And into her bath with no worry or tears,
And saw she was spotless behind both her ears.
And when she came home on the Bakerloo line,
With her imports and exports of old Argentine,
His eyes seemed to say, 'If you get that work
      done
Then we can go out for our romp in the sun!'

So that is the tale of the girl I once knew,
Who now is as sensibly punctual as you.
And here's the most curious episode in it:
Veronica managed to love every minute!

                                    Charlotte Hough

Vicky

A javelin thrower called Vicky
Found the grip of her javelin sticky.
When it came to the throw
She just couldn't let go –
Making judging the distance quite tricky.

Michael Palin

Wet playtime

Wayne has lost his slippers
He left 'em on his chair
Liza Wilson saw 'em
At playtime they was there
Martin Doughty touched 'em
he threw them near the sink
he threw them in the corner
cos' he said they made a stink
Debbie saw him do it
and the dinner lady knows
she stood him in the corner
right next to Billy Rose

the dinner lady's angry
the playground lady's cross
one's shouting in the lobby
and the other's caught Paul Ross
Paul Ross – he had the slipper
John James caused all the noise
and they're standing by the staffroom
with thirty other boys . . .
Five have lost their sarnies
Five have lost their coats
Five have found some sarnies
and five have found five coats

three have lost the hamster
two know where it's hid
and Emma's in the dustbin
And Sarah's thrown the lid . . .
        it's another wet-time playtime
        a day of all 'being in'

        the game's called 'catch the culprit'
And teachers never win!

Peter Dixon

I hate

I hate the way my mum calls me 'Wend'.
I've got nothing to do!
I've played all my games and read all my books –
What can I do?

I hate my Dad when he's buried in the paper.
'What can I do Dad?'
It's raining and it's cold, I can't go out –
What can I do?

I hate all these fish, when they gulp
Through the glass.
I've nothing to do!
All I can think of is to make faces back
– That's what I'll do.

Wendy Snape

William

William stayed at home today, his tummy hurt
(he said)
He thought he had a backache too, and had to
stay in bed
The doctor came and humm'd and ha'd and
wrote him out a note
For Mum to get some pills for him – 'they'll also
help his throat'.

William hugged his teddy bear, and smiled a
secret smile
'It's cold and wet and grey outside – I'll stay up
here a while
They'll bring me drinks and things to eat, no one
will even think
That actually I'm quite OK, in fact I'm in the
pink.'

You see yesterday, at hometime, the big boy in
Class 2
Saw William pinch his sister and make her black
and blue
He said he'd tell the teacher and that she would
tell the Head
So William's lying low, in the safety of his bed.

Mary Rudin

Where's my dictionary?

Xerxes and Xanthe
Sailed to Xonotla
In a beautiful Xebec
With a splendid Xoanon

Xanthe saw a Xeme
And Xerxes
Caught a Xiphias
While drinking Xeres

When they reached Xonotla
Xerxes played the xylophone
In the Xystus
And Xanthe picked a Xynid
For Xmas

Benjamin Bolt

From The wicked children's alphabet

Yvonne, who was nearly ten,
Had a lovely fountain pen
From her favourite Uncle Frank,
Who got it at the Midland Bank.

But her brother Zachary
Dipped it in his father's tea.
Father had such stomach pains
Mother sent for Doctor Vanes.

Doctor sent him straight to bed,
And now he's turned a blue-ish red.

Pauline Mitchell

The Poet Sings The Passing Of His Love

When Zoe's shop was simply labelled 'LUNCHES'
I took her roses every day in bunches.
But now she's changed it to 'YE LUNCHEON
    SHOPPE'
I've sent her one symbolic final poppe.

Richard Usborne

Index of children's names

Index of first lines

Acknowledgements

The editors and publishers would like to thank the following for permission to use copyright material in this collection. The publishers have made every effort to contact the copyright holders but there are a few cases where it has not been possible to do so. We would be grateful to hear from anyone who can enable us to contact them so the omission can be corrected at the first opportunity.

Angus and Robertson (UK) Ltd for 'Nomenclature' by Peter Wesley Smith from the *Ombley-Gombley*.

The Bodley Head for 'Happy Birthday, Dilroy' by John Agard from *I Din Do Nuttin*.

Curits Brown Ltd for 'Veronica' by Charlotte Hough from *Verse and Various*.

Jonathan Cape Ltd for 'The last word of a bluebird' by Robert Frost from *The Poetry of Robert Frost* edited by Edward Connery Lathem and 'Shaking' and 'Hector the collector' by Shel Silverstein from *A Light in the Attic* and *Where the Sidewalk Ends*.

Collins Publishers for 'Mandy likes the mud' and 'Sally won't you walk with me?' by Gareth Owen.

Rosemary Cowan for 'Kite Flying', 'Next Year' and 'For Sophie'.

J. M. Dent & Sons Ltd for 'George's pet' and 'Harry the hawk' by Margaret Mahy from *Nonstop Nonsense*.

Andre Deutsch Ltd for 'I say' by Michael Rosen from *You Can't Catch Me* and 'The sniffle' by Ogden Nash from *Parents Keep Out*.

Peter Dixon for 'Charles' and 'Wet Playtime'.

Louise Draycott for 'Lost love' and 'Penny'.

Gerald Duckworth & Co Ltd for 'Rebecca' and 'Tarantella' by Hilaire Belloc from *Sonnets and Verse*.

The English Centre for 'New Shoes' by Michelle Campbell and 'The Production Line' by Bobby Pearce from *City Limits*.

Janet E. Faulks for 'Problem Child'.

Roy Fuller for 'Teresa Nude' from *Seen Grandpa Lately?*.

Heinemann Educational Books for 'Marbles' by Sarah Edenbrow from *Young Writers 26th Year*.

McGraw Hill Ryerson for 'White Cat' by Raymond Kinster from *Collected Poems*.

Hodder & Stoughton Ltd for 'More thoughts from a little boy' by Rod Hull from *The Reluctant Pote*.

Century Hutchinson Ltd for 'Little Barbara', 'When Jilly eats jelly', 'Luke', 'Natalie' and 'Nicola' by Colin West from *Not to be Taken Seriously*; 'My sister is missing' by Colin West from *A Step in the Wrong Direction*; 'Caroline in cotton rags' by Colin West and 'Dawn', 'Jeff', 'Owen' and 'Vicky' by Michael Palin from *Limericks*.

Tom May for 'Come Home Alexandra'.

Pauline Mitchell for 'Emily', 'Quentin' and 'Yvonne' from *The Wicked Children's Alphabet*.

John Murray (Publishers) Ltd for 'Hunter trials' by John Betjeman from *Collected Poems*.

Barry Norrington for 'Ben'.

Emma Payne for 'Night' and 'Boy in bubbles'.

Reproduced by permission of Penguin Books Ltd 'Colin' and 'Blame' from *Please Mrs Butler* by Alan Ahlberg (Kestrel Books, 1983), copyright © 1983 by Alan Ahlberg; 'Embrionic mega-stars' from *Gargling with Jelly* by Brian Patten (Viking Kestrel Books, 1985), copyright © Brian Pattern, 1985; 'Ian said' from *You Tell Me* poems by Roger McGough and Michael Rosen (Kestrel Books, 1979), Michael Rosen poems copyright © 1979 by Michael Rosen, selection copyright © 1979 by Penguin Books Ltd; 'Nothing, that's what' from *Wry Rhymes for Troublesome Times* by Max Fatchen (Kestrel Books, 1983), copyright © 1983 by Max Fatchen; 'There was a young fellow called Hugh' and 'Little John was not content' from *Songs for my Dog and Other People* by Max Fatchen (Kestrel Books, 1980), copyright © 1980 by Max Fatchen and 'The tale of Custard the